My 30 Day Prayer Journal & Planner:
30 Days To Fine Tune You
In Prayer, Purpose, And Productivity.

Send inquiries and letters to the author:
Faerie Grace
PO BOX 98
Crabtree, PA 15624
Copyright owner may also be found at FaerieGrace.com
First paperback edition April 2021

Paperback: ISBN 978-1-7361031-0-4

Edited by Sam Wright Writes
Cover art and illustrations by Leanne Roux
Journal Design Layout by Liliana Kayal
Formatting by Ibrahim Mahmud

Send mail to
Faerie Grace
P.O. BOX 98
Crabtree, PA 15624

Feel free to give a review if you enjoyed this planner.
We thank you.
Faerie Grace is available for speaking events
FaerieGrace.com

This Prayer Journal and Planner belongs to;

Smile and have an amazing happy day!

My 30 Day Planner

Month: ____________________

SUNDAY	MONDAY	TUESDAY	WEDNESDAY

Year: ____________

THURSDAY	FRIDAY	SATURDAY	NOTES

HOW TO USE

"May he grant your heart's desires and make all your plans succeed."
- Psalm 20:4

3 Goals Today

Setting three goals a day is like an archer shooting his arrows. He puts a target out there, one within reach of his aim and his focus. BOOM! You are much more likely to hit your target (goals) when you know what they are. Writing your goals out will be your three achievable targets each day.

Your personalized targets can be big goals, medium goals or small goals. The size doesn't matter. Getting them done does. Celebrate each one you accomplish no matter the size, as they are all important to your success, personal growth, and dreams.

Scientifically, when you write your goals out, you are triggering three parts of your brain, making it more likely you actually achieve the goals and dreams floating around in your head and heart. (Matthew 17:20)

3 Things I'm Thankful For

Having a heart of thanks moves mountains. It also heals broken pieces in our mind, spirit, and heart. I do this with our youngest son. I started it when we were going through a very trying time in our lives. God spoke to my heart when it was shattered, "A thankful heart heals a troubled mind." I immediately said out loud what I was thankful for. It trumped all the pain that was aching me paralyzed. Still to this day, when I am overwhelmed, distraught, or fiercely grumpy, I speak out loud things I am thankful for. Boom! Works every time. My spirit calms, it softens, and I re-center. If you write out something you are thankful for, it will speak to your mind, spirit, and heart. It will start healing and move mountains you once thought impossible. I'm thankful you are reading this. (1 Thessalonians 5:18)

3 Phone Calls to Make

We seem to all dread making phone calls as if we were telemarketers getting hung up on with a vengeance. Nowadays, this weird phenomenon is heightened. Everyone just texts, even in the business realm! I have caught myself calling people less because I don't want them to feel obligated to talk with me! What?! We have silly notions sometimes. However, the reality, we do dread some phone calls we must make as adults. Some tips for phone calls I dread to make for one reason or another, I put my earbuds in; that way, I can be doing other things while I wait on hold for six years. Then I, for some reason, feel I am getting a bonus round to whatever else I choose to do while I wait on hold, paint my nails, sweep my floor, organize my suitcase, I mean purse. If no one is home, meaning I won't disturb anyone around me with sound, I will put my phone on speakerphone, the same effect as earbuds. I can be on hold or talk to someone while I do other things.

Positive phone calls I dread making for other reasons, like catch up with a relative or friend but know I might be on the phone for a while, I have exercised hula-hooped or gone for a walk or done the dishes. That's two birds with one stone! Boom! It doesn't feel like time wasted, but instead motivated me to get something else done that I was dreading too! Ha-ha. The key is not dreading. Dreading sucks up our mental power like a hungry polka dot monster. Don't let dread have any of your superpower. Use your mental power to move mountains! Be positive! Feel empowered. Pretend your someone in high authority, famous, etc. Have fun with your phone call.

Now don't call as an arrogant butthead, lol. But do call with authority and kindness wrapped together.

Phone calls can feel like such a task and WORK! Ugh! BUT if we make three phone calls a day, it's achievable and will move mountains in our lives to be organized, productive, and successful. Don't be overwhelmed, my friend. Just pick up the phone, be bold, straighten your posture, put a smile on your face and speak, you adorable Diva. "Hello?" (Colossians 4:6)

3 Powerful Affirmation

I'll be honest, although I made this prayer journal believing in it and using it myself, writing down affirmations was of no interest to me. It felt like pulling teeth to let myself think of something, let alone write it down. I felt as if I was bragging or trying to be boastful, which is not my character. So, I just kept ignoring that part. I think I even made tiny audible groans as my pen in hand skirted around it. I said to myself, "Listen, one day you are going to sell this journal. If you don't use it correctly, how can you expect others to do it and believe?" I grumbled under my breath with a small eye roll; I was taking myself back to teenager days. Sorry for all those eye rolls, parents. I struggled to think of something. "What was I going to brag about...?" As I felt that's all it was, telling how great I was. I mean, the Bible says, "Don't brag about yourself, let someone else do it. Not yourself." -FRV. (Faerie's Roundabout Version) But then a lightbulb went off. "How can others believe in who you are or want to be if you're too shy or humble to think about them or speak them out?" I nodded my head. And Boom! I was confident in saying who I wanted to be. I have plenty of insecurities. I get the fraud complex like everyone else. It's not that I don't believe positive things about myself. It's the level I lack to want to claim it. I'm not where I want to be in anything! But deep down, I also believe in myself. So, off I went; I sat and wrote three bold affirmations about myself. Giving myself the freedom to say, "I know I'm not at the level I want, but I'm getting there; therefore, I speak as if I am, because I will be!" You know what? It felt amazing to write it as if it was so! I smiled big. I felt empowered just by saying it then writing it down! I felt it. I believed it. So, my friend, write out your powerhouse affirmations. I already see them! <3 (Proverbs 23:7)

Healthy Yummy Snacks and Meals

This is not my natural state or menu. I love sweets, carbs... better yet, make that "I love sweet carbs." (mouth salivating) Oh Lord, I think that's the French in me. Croissant? Crepe? Or the Dutch in me, we grew up on buttered bread with chocolate sprinkles at Oma's house. Followed with a cup of instant coffee my older sister and I would make within the first couple hours at Oma's. Yes, I've been drinking coffee since the tender age of 4. Actually, many of us have a sweet tooth. My mom's brother has a kitchen that looks like Willy Wonka decorated it. Oh, how I smile at the memory of it. He has no Dutch or French in him. He's all Spanish. I guess it doesn't matter your nationality. Some of us are super sweet in this life and I think it has to do with how much sugar we are consuming.

But now, being a mom, I slowed down for the sake of being a positive influence on my children and providing good meals and snacks for them. It's unnatural for me. BUT I want a right life. To get that, I need to make the right choices.

I highly recommend substitutes. Take out pop and put it in carbonated water. Make a transition. Then go from carbonated water to just water. Then do filtered water. Risqué? Add lemon or lime or ginger! Boom! Progression. I did candy bars as meals back in the day as a single career businesswoman! I went from candy bars as my meals when I was on the run. Let's just say commercials convinced me of this choice. "Need a break? Hangry?" Yes and Yes! Plus, it had nuts in it? Nuts are healthy! But then I transitioned to the candy bars in health stores. (sarcasm voice to self, "Way to be a grownup") After that, I switched to the best choices of bars at the health stores. Some were just as yummy or even yummier than my candy bar worldly choices! Some I wanted to wrap and put back on the shelf. They should be ashamed of themselves! IF I wanted something that tasted that bad, I would have eaten broccoli. Sorry, broc. I took things a step further by switching to making homemade treats with all healthy ingredients with semi-sweet cocoa. I was satisfied. Honestly, I do not even crave candy bars anymore. My sweet tooth is now hungering healthy sweet snacks that are good for me and make me feel energized after consumption.

You got this! Take baby steps. I can do carrots with ranch and a yummy pizza to go with it. I actually celebrate when I eat carrots! Whoo-hoo!!

I cut back on the ranch, make the pizza with healthy dough, and put healthier toppings on. I went from fried chicken to grilled chicken: another small progression in the right direction. I bought my bread machine from a thrift store for $10. Boom! Winning. I also have healthy people in my life. I let them bring me snacks and drinks and I make healthier choices when they visit me.

I know you can find healthy substitutes and get the same satisfaction to your taste buds. It just might take some trial and error.

Writing the snacks and meals down is KEY! When you are hungry it is the worst time to think. If you're human, you will just grab something processed and cheap. The hunger bugs will cloud your judgment!

You are thinking, "How much longer is she going to talk about snacks? Isn't this a prayer journal?" Last snack story. I struggle to eat a whole apple. I struggle to bite into an apple. Maybe that's the princess in me though. I do have a mighty nice prince who would kiss me back to life, I think, but why take the risk? Yet, I found if I put caramel, chocolate and cashews on my apple, BOOM! Amazing! That is one trick I just have to do. My sweetheart husband took me to a farm selling homegrown produce and we bought their highly recommended apples. Yes, I ate one! Well, ok. . . I confess. . . ¼ without any toppings on it. It was work for me. But I did it. The drive was an hour, but it was worth it. Perhaps you need to travel to a local farmer's market. I love homegrown strawberries and tomatoes; the stores cannot hold a candle to the freshness of something grown local. Try the fresh local version before you judge or someone that knows how to prepare food in an awesome way. Yes, I have tried local homegrown broccoli... I'm still waiting to be swayed.

Small steps are better than no steps and each step does make a difference. Do the substitutes. Progression. Keep walking in the right direction and enjoy the learning and experience journey. If you have any good substitute tips, write them on our Facebook wall. We thank you in advance. Till then, right them in your journal! (Genesis 1:29).

Prayer Needs/Wants

Should I explain why we should write down our prayer needs and wants? Prayer moves mountains. Prayer changes lives, period. If you read the Bible for even a moment, you will see how the prayers of a man or woman changed the course of their life or those they loved. Pray, pray, pray! Pray without ceasing was one of the last words my mom would ever tell me. She told me that, and the 2nd to last time I saw her, she was praying with all her heart and prayer language. However, that story is for another book.

Some people will say, "You can't ask God for things!" Why not? Of course, you can. Did Jesus ask God for stuff? You bet'cha! Does your child ask you for stuff? You listen and you answer, don't you? The answers you give are for the child and their best interest, correct? Yes! Of course, correct. Same with God. (Matthew 7:11) He created you. He cares what you want, just like you created your little minis and want to give them the world. And He's (God) so much cooler and better than us because he knows what we want or need before we even ask. I wish I could have that superpower with my teenagers. It would save a lot on guesswork and time.

Ask Him. He cares (1 Thessalonians 5:16-18).

My son asked me, "I don't know how to pray." I responded, "It's just talking to him like you talk to me. Be open, honest, and frank. Be you! He already knows and He wants to hear from you. He's waiting." I tell you the same, just talk to God. He knows it all anyhow. Don't try to fool him or feel the need to hide or lie about anything. It can't be done anyhow; He knows it all, it's ok. He's all ears and open heart waiting for you. I promise (John 14:14).

Memory Verse of the Week

This is powerful.

Getting scripture in your heart is priceless. It's life-changing. Each scripture you memorize is like putting on a new piece of amour in your everyday life. When things attack you, you're covered. It feels amazing to speak power when you feel week. Writing them down helps get them into your soul and memory. Trust me it feels good as you write them down (2 Corinthians 10:4).

Day: Date:

If you are like me, I lose track of the day and date. Writing it down each day helps me remember things better and where I am in life as well as jogging my memory of a special event or occasion that day (Psalm 118:24).

Kick Butt To-Do List

This is the same as the three main goals, except these are smaller tasks. Write down things you have to get done for normal everyday life. I list things like chiropractor appointment, grocery store, and Post Office. The great thing about making this list is getting to CHECK it off! When we check things off our to-do list, it releases endorphins that make us feel good inside. So, keep it going! For me personally, I would put in my first block: Make my bed. It's simple. It gets the ball rolling. You're unstoppable! (Philippians 4:13)

5 Min Prayer 10 Min Bible Read 15 Min Walk....

I get overwhelmed with all the things I want to do. 1. Because I have so much to do each day and 2. I feel guilty doing some of the things I want to do. But we need to do things that refuel us. It's vital to sustain our beautiful spirit. So, what I do is break everything down into little time slots. That way, I don't feel guilty for doing what I want. I feed my soul and personal wants and goals. And things I know I need to do but put off or dread. Putting them on paper for a little time makes it seem do-able because it is. "Ok, just do it for 10 min." I don't feel overwhelmed or guilty to do them. Break it down. Anything is manageable if you break it into small pieces. For bigger tasks, I'll ask myself, "How long will it take?" Then I will block out the time, making a start time and end time. This helps me not feel overwhelmed. Why? Because I see my start time and I see my end time. "Ok, I won't be doing this the rest of my life. There's light at the end of the tunnel." I feel hope! And off the timer goes and off I go!

Fill in the empty spaces with important things, such as music lessons, family time, or career targets. Or write things you dread, but you block out time to see it will not be forever! Yay! Remember to fill in with things you want to do as well. There are endless possibilities for the empty "min" blocks (Ephesians 5:15-17).

15 Min Give back

When we do things for others, we feel amazing. They feel amazing. It's a win-win as we breathe life into ourselves and them at the same time. Who knows the trickling effect from there? Giving just 15 minutes of your time to someone else is powerful. This can be spending time with a child, visiting a nursing home, or getting groceries for someone else. It can be making your favorite cookies and delivering them to people or an organization.

Personally, I like to set this time aside to sit at my desk and handwrite cards or take packages to the post office to mail to people. Why? Because it's on my heart, it's a natural gift the Lord gave me. What gift do you have (2 Corinthians 6:8), that you can give back to others? (Ephesians 2:10)
Write them down though, so they happen! Writing them down reminds you, sets the ball rolling, and holds you accountable.

P.S if you want a letter, let me know and as time permits, I will mail you a card. (Proverbs 27:17)

Pray For

This may seem like a repeat because we already have a PRAYER NEEDS/WANTS section. This, however, is different. This blank is specifically for people's names. People the Lord has put on your heart. People you want to see salvation for. My aunt believes someone prayed for her, my dad, my mom, and their other brothers and sisters, basically my whole family while all 16 children grew up together playing in the park on their street. The Lord put that in her heart. I am thankful for that person. What a seed planted in my family line, on both sides of my family! We will know for sure in heaven. But the blessing before we go to heaven is, I get to reap those effects as well, and so do my children. What a blessing.

Who can you pray for? Change someone's life! Change someone's family line. Wow! Think how powerful that is. (James 5:16) P.S now this part shouldn't be work. The Lord will put someone or people on your heart. And you can ask Him, "Who do you want me to pray for?" I know of a man who each year picks three men to pray for. He and those he has prayed for have seen nothing short of miracles happen in their lives. Coincidence? Some might say. (smirk) I'm not one of them, though (James 5:16)

Goals and Focus for Tomorrow

Congratulate yourself for an awesome job today! You made leaps and bounds in many areas. Even your baby steps are making way to a powerful journey of greatness and peace. Never forget, my friend, every step in the right direction is a powerful one! Celebrate yourself. Now write out the main focus and things you want to achieve and kick butt tomorrow. By thinking about them and writing them down, you have set the ball in motion to a beautiful, positive, and productive day. This sets you ahead of the game for tomorrow before tomorrow even starts because while you are sleeping, your subconscious will go to work for you and think of ways to accomplish what you just thought about and wrote down before bed. Boom! I call that a bonus round with no effort. It's like residual income! (Proverbs 16:3)

30 Day Prayer Journal

There are, 30 journal pages to write as you feel led. I wrote on the top of each page, in hopes to get the ball rolling with ideas, thoughts, and inspiration. Be organic with what you write. Do not hold back, this is a safe place, a welcoming place to let your thoughts and dreams take flight. On the rough days, it is to unleash them on paper and give them to The Creator! He does not want you to carry the burdens of the world. (Matthew 11:28)

The journal page is large and plentiful. I personally have filled my pages with all kinds of craziness. Oh, friend if only you could see. (Maybe one day I will post such a page for amusement) You can use just half the page, date it, and use the other half for the next journal entry. (That idea is for my conservative, coupon cutting, thrift store friends.) Other days you may have a surplus to write for whatever reason, good or bad, and you need two journal pages! Do it! I am a true believer if you do what you feel led to, assuming you're balanced, you will make the right choice. Don't hold yourself back is all I am saying. This is your journal, whether you paid for it or it was a gift, it is yours to do with what you want. Even if you stole it, it's still your journal. Lol. Acquiring it illegally and unjustly, it's still yours. God is a gracious God, mercy trumps judgment. Maybe you will use your journal and then have an eye-opening moment and transformation. YOU, oh beautiful one, will start a ministry to help those who struggle with poverty, or thievery, or whatever hang up you had. You see God takes even the bad we do and makes it good. If we allow him. That rabbit trail was for someone. I know it, and I'm speaking to your past, let it go my friend (2 Corinthians 5:17) (Hebrews 8:12)

This is a 30 day journal because they say it takes 21 days to make a habit. Sometimes we need a little help, a little push, a little guidance, to do the right things we are called to. I believe this journal will help you get into the healthy habits you want to. Opening the door to an amazing, balanced, and anointed life.

P.S I did not edit this last paragraph; it is raw, it is me, and unedited. Why? Well, main reason, I already paid the editor and I forgot to add this part. Ha-Ha! But it also is an opportunity to be transparent with you. We all need help in some areas. For me, more areas than not.

Thank you for letting me be real, be myself. To let go of the spirit of perfectionism that can hold us back. I give you permission to do the same! (Psalm 139:14) May this Prayer journal be a steppingstone to unleashing the powerful beautiful soul within you.

I believe in your Dreams and Life.

Love, Your Faerie Grace

Faerie
Grace

Date ______________________ Day ______________________.

3 Goals today

-
-
-

3 Things I'm thankful for

-
-
-

3 Phone calls to make

-
-
-

3 Powerful Affirmation

-
-
-

Healthy yummy snacks & meals

- [ ]
- [ ]
- [ ]
- [ ]
- [ ]
- [ ]

Prayer Needs/Wants

Memory verse of the week: ______________________

Kick butt To-do list

- [ ]
- [ ]
- [ ]
- [ ]
- [ ]
- [ ]

- [ ] 5 min Prayer
- [ ] 10 min Bible Read
- [ ] 15 min Walk
- [ ] 30 min Me Time
- [ ] min ______
- [ ] min ______
- [ ] min ______
- [ ] min ______

15 min Give back:

Pray For:

Goals and focus for tomorrow

Sweet dreams beautiful.
You were amazing Today!

Be bold! Ask! Imagine!
Dream my friend. Write down all that you want.
Imagine it true.
Dream a little bigger.

"The LORD will work out his plans for my life— for your faithful love, O LORD, endures forever. Don't abandon me, for you made me."

Psalms 138:8

Date ______________ Day ______________.

3 Goals today

-
-
-

3 Things I'm thankful for

-
-
-

3 Phone calls to make

-
-
-

3 Powerful Affirmation

-
-
-

Healthy yummy snacks & meals

- [ ]
- [ ]
- [ ]
- [ ]
- [ ]
- [ ]

Prayer Needs/Wants

Memory verse of the week:

Kick butt To-do list

- [ ]
- [ ]
- [ ]
- [ ]
- [ ]
- [ ]

- [ ] 5 min Prayer
- [ ] 10 min Bible Read
- [ ] 15 min Walk
- [ ] 30 min Me Time
- [ ] min
- [ ] min
- [ ] min
- [ ] min

15 min Give back:

Pray For:

Goals and focus for tomorrow

Sweet dreams beautiful.
You were amazing Today!

Write down all the things you think
are impossible but you desperately want to achieve.
Remember, it is POSSIBLE, because HE is with you.

"With man this is impossible, but not with God;
all things are possible with God."

Mark 10:27

Date ____________ Day ____________.

3 Goals today

-
-
-

Prayer Needs/Wants

Memory verse of the week:

3 Things I'm thankful for

-
-
-

Kick butt To-do list

- ☐
- ☐
- ☐
- ☐
- ☐
- ☐

3 Phone calls to make

-
-
-

3 Powerful Affirmation

-
-
-

Healthy yummy snacks & meals

☐ ☐
☐ ☐
☐ ☐

☐ 5 min Prayer	☐ min
☐ 10 min Bible Read	☐ min
☐ 15 min Walk	☐ min
☐ 30 min Me Time	☐ min

15 min Give back:

Pray For:

Goals and focus for tomorrow

Sweet dreams beautiful.
You were amazing Today!

Write down all your anxieties and fears.
Writing them down gets them off your heart and mind. Looking at them on paper lets you see that they are manageable.

"Cast all your anxiety on him because he cares for you."

Peter 5:7

Date ______________ Day ______________.

3 Goals today

-
-
-

Prayer Needs/Wants

Memory verse of the week:

3 Things I'm thankful for

-
-
-

Kick butt To-do list

- [ ]
- [ ]
- [ ]
- [ ]
- [ ]
- [ ]

3 Phone calls to make

-
-
-

3 Powerful Affirmation

-
-
-

- [ ] 5 min Prayer
- [ ] 10 min Bible Read
- [ ] 15 min Walk
- [ ] 30 min Me Time
- [ ] min
- [ ] min
- [ ] min
- [ ] min

Healthy yummy snacks & meals

- [ ]
- [ ]
- [ ]
- [ ]
- [ ]
- [ ]

15 min Give back:

Pray For:

Goals and focus for tomorrow

Sweet dreams beautiful.
You were amazing Today!

Good Morning!
Things that make me feel and see beauty all around me. . .

"The faithful love of the Lord never ends!
His mercies never cease. Great is his faithfulness;
his mercies begin afresh each morning."
Lamentations 3:22-23 -NLT

Date ________________ Day ________________.

3 Goals today

-
-
-

3 Things I'm thankful for

-
-
-

3 Phone calls to make

-
-
-

3 Powerful Affirmation

-
-
-

Healthy yummy snacks & meals

- [ ]
- [ ]
- [ ]
- [ ]
- [ ]
- [ ]

Prayer Needs/Wants

Memory verse of the week:

Kick butt To-do list

- [ ]
- [ ]
- [ ]
- [ ]
- [ ]
- [ ]

- [ ] 5 min Prayer
- [ ] 10 min Bible Read
- [ ] 15 min Walk
- [ ] 30 min Me Time

- [ ] min
- [ ] min
- [ ] min
- [ ] min

15 min Give back:

Pray For:

Goals and focus for tomorrow

Sweet dreams beautiful.
You were amazing Today!

What are some things I can do for my friends this week to show I care for them and love them?

"Greater love has no one than this:
to lay down one's life for one's
friends. "

John 15:13

Date ____________________ Day ____________________.

3 Goals today

-
-
-

3 Things I'm thankful for

-
-
-

3 Phone calls to make

-
-
-

3 Powerful Affirmation

-
-
-

Healthy yummy snacks & meals

- [ ]
- [ ]
- [ ]
- [ ]
- [ ]
- [ ]

Prayer Needs/Wants

Memory verse of the week:

Kick butt To-do list

- [ ]
- [ ]
- [ ]
- [ ]
- [ ]
- [ ]

- [ ] 5 min Prayer
- [ ] 10 min Bible Read
- [ ] 15 min Walk
- [ ] 30 min Me Time
- [ ] min
- [ ] min
- [ ] min
- [ ] min

15 min Give back:

Pray For:

Goals and focus for tomorrow

Sweet dreams beautiful.
You were amazing Today!

I'm asking God for
these Big things today!

"Now to him who is able to do immeasurably more than all we ask or imagine, according to his power that is at work within us."

Ephesians 3:20

Date ____________ Day ____________.

3 Goals today

-
-
-

3 Things I'm thankful for

-
-
-

3 Phone calls to make

-
-
-

3 Powerful Affirmation

-
-
-

Healthy yummy snacks & meals

- [ ]
- [ ]
- [ ]
- [ ]
- [ ]
- [ ]

Prayer Needs/Wants

Memory verse of the week:

Kick butt To-do list

- [ ]
- [ ]
- [ ]
- [ ]
- [ ]
- [ ]

- [ ] 5 min Prayer
- [ ] 10 min Bible Read
- [ ] 15 min Walk
- [ ] 30 min Me Time

- [ ] min
- [ ] min
- [ ] min
- [ ] min

15 min Give back:

Pray For:

Goals and focus for tomorrow

Sweet dreams beautiful.
You were amazing Today!

My Strengths are. . .

"Be strong and courageous. Do not be afraid or terrified because of them, for the Lord your God goes with you; he will never leave you nor forsake you."

Deuteronomy 31:6

Date ______________________ Day ______________________.

3 Goals today

-
-
-

3 Things I'm thankful for

-
-
-

3 Phone calls to make

-
-
-

3 Powerful Affirmation

-
-
-

Healthy yummy snacks & meals

- [ ]
- [ ]
- [ ]
- [ ]
- [ ]
- [ ]

Prayer Needs/Wants

Memory verse of the week:

Kick butt To-do list

- [ ]
- [ ]
- [ ]
- [ ]
- [ ]
- [ ]

- [ ] 5 min Prayer
- [ ] 10 min Bible Read
- [ ] 15 min Walk
- [ ] 30 min Me Time

- [ ] min
- [ ] min
- [ ] min
- [ ] min

15 min Give back:

Pray For:

Goals and focus for tomorrow

Sweet dreams beautiful.
You were amazing Today!

I fear not, for God is with me.
What fears am I giving to the Lord TODAY?
Things to never look at again, for He is my protector.

"The LORD is my light and my salvation— so why should I be afraid? The LORD is my fortress, protecting me from danger, so why should I tremble?"

Psalms 27:1 - NLT

Date ______________________ Day ______________________.

3 Goals today

-
-
-

3 Things I'm thankful for

-
-
-

3 Phone calls to make

-
-
-

3 Powerful Affirmation

-
-
-

Healthy yummy snacks & meals

- [ ]
- [ ]
- [ ]
- [ ]
- [ ]
- [ ]

Prayer Needs/Wants

Memory verse of the week:

Kick butt To-do list

- [ ]
- [ ]
- [ ]
- [ ]
- [ ]
- [ ]

- [ ] 5 min Prayer
- [ ] 10 min Bible Read
- [ ] 15 min Walk
- [ ] 30 min Me Time
- [ ] min
- [ ] min
- [ ] min
- [ ] min

15 min Give back:

Pray For:

Goals and focus for tomorrow

Sweet dreams beautiful.
You were amazing Today!

How can I delight in the Lord today?
What are the desires of my heart?

Take delight in the LORD,
and he will give you the desires of your heart.
Psalm 37:4

Date ____________________ Day ____________________.

3 Goals today

-
-
-

3 Things I'm thankful for

-
-
-

3 Phone calls to make

-
-
-

3 Powerful Affirmation

-
-
-

Healthy yummy snacks & meals

☐ ☐
☐ ☐
☐ ☐

Prayer Needs/Wants

Memory verse of the week:

Kick butt To-do list

☐
☐
☐
☐
☐
☐

☐ 5 min Prayer ☐ min
☐ 10 min Bible Read ☐ min
☐ 15 min Walk ☐ min
☐ 30 min Me Time ☐ min

15 min Give back:

Pray For:

Goals and focus for tomorrow

Sweet dreams beautiful.
You were amazing Today!

Today I am ASKING for. . .
Today I am SEEKING for. . .
Today I am KNOCKING on these doors. . .

"Ask and it will be given to you; seek and you will find; knock and the door will be opened to you."
Matthew 7:7

Date ____________________ Day ____________________.

3 Goals today

-
-
-

Prayer Needs/Wants

Memory verse of the week:

3 Things I'm thankful for

-
-
-

Kick butt To-do list

- [ ]
- [ ]
- [ ]
- [ ]
- [ ]
- [ ]

3 Phone calls to make

-
-
-

3 Powerful Affirmation

-
-
-

- [ ] 5 min Prayer
- [ ] 10 min Bible Read
- [ ] 15 min Walk
- [ ] 30 min Me Time
- [ ] min
- [ ] min
- [ ] min
- [ ] min

Healthy yummy snacks & meals

- [ ]
- [ ]
- [ ]
- [ ]
- [ ]
- [ ]

15 min Give back:

Pray For:

Goals and focus for tomorrow

Sweet dreams beautiful.
You were amazing Today!

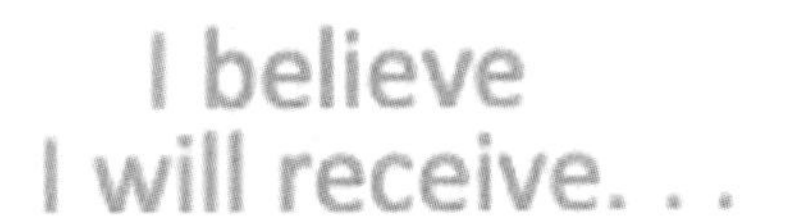

"If you believe, you will receive whatever you ask for in prayer."

Matthew 21:22

Date ______________________ Day ______________________.

3 Goals today

-
-
-

3 Things I'm thankful for

-
-
-

3 Phone calls to make

-
-
-

3 Powerful Affirmation

-
-
-

Healthy yummy snacks & meals

☐ ☐
☐ ☐
☐ ☐

Prayer Needs/Wants

Memory verse of the week:

Kick butt To-do list

☐
☐
☐
☐
☐
☐

☐ 5 min Prayer ☐ min
☐ 10 min Bible Read ☐ min
☐ 15 min Walk ☐ min
☐ 30 min Me Time ☐ min

15 min Give back:

Pray For:

Goals and focus for tomorrow

Sweet dreams beautiful.
You were amazing Today!

In these ways I will speak life today. . .

"The tongue has the power of life and death, and those who love it will eat its fruit."

Proverbs 18:21

Date ______________________ Day ______________________.

3 Goals today

-
-
-

3 Things I'm thankful for

-
-
-

3 Phone calls to make

-
-
-

3 Powerful Affirmation

-
-
-

Healthy yummy snacks & meals

☐ ☐
☐ ☐
☐ ☐

Prayer Needs/Wants

Memory verse of the week:

Kick butt To-do list

☐
☐
☐
☐
☐
☐

☐ 5 min Prayer ☐ min
☐ 10 min Bible Read ☐ min
☐ 15 min Walk ☐ min
☐ 30 min Me Time ☐ min

15 min Give back:

Pray For:

Goals and focus for tomorrow

Sweet dreams beautiful.
You were amazing Today!

I will have Joy because. . .
I will have Peace because. . .
I will have Hope because. . .

"May the God of hope fill you with all joy and peace as you trust in him, so that you may overflow with hope by the power of the Holy Spirit."

Romans 15:13

Date ____________________ Day ____________________.

3 Goals today

-
-
-

3 Things I'm thankful for

-
-
-

3 Phone calls to make

-
-
-

3 Powerful Affirmation

-
-
-

Healthy yummy snacks & meals

- [ ]
- [ ]
- [ ]
- [ ]
- [ ]
- [ ]

Prayer Needs/Wants

Memory verse of the week:

Kick butt To-do list

- [ ]
- [ ]
- [ ]
- [ ]
- [ ]
- [ ]

- [ ] 5 min Prayer
- [ ] min
- [ ] 10 min Bible Read
- [ ] min
- [ ] 15 min Walk
- [ ] min
- [ ] 30 min Me Time
- [ ] min

15 min Give back:

Pray For:

Goals and focus for tomorrow

Sweet dreams beautiful.
You were amazing Today!

I am going to do great things today!

“I can do all this through him who gives me strength.”
Philippians 4:13

Date ______________ Day ______________.

3 Goals today

-
-
-

Prayer Needs/Wants

Memory verse of the week:

3 Things I'm thankful for

-
-
-

Kick butt To-do list

- [ ]
- [ ]
- [ ]
- [ ]
- [ ]
- [ ]

3 Phone calls to make

-
-
-

3 Powerful Affirmation

-
-
-

- [ ] 5 min Prayer
- [ ] 10 min Bible Read
- [ ] 15 min Walk
- [ ] 30 min Me Time
- [ ] min
- [ ] min
- [ ] min
- [ ] min

Healthy yummy snacks & meals

- [ ]
- [ ]
- [ ]
- [ ]
- [ ]
- [ ]

15 min Give back:

Pray For:

Goals and focus for tomorrow

Sweet dreams beautiful.
You were amazing Today!

Here are my plans. I believe in them!
I understand I am called for greatness and to just be ME!

"Trust in the Lord with all your heart; do not depend on your own understanding. Seek his will in all you do, and he will show you which path to take."

Proverbs 3:5-6 - NLT

Date ______________ Day ______________.

3 Goals today

-
-
-

3 Things I'm thankful for

-
-
-

3 Phone calls to make

-
-
-

3 Powerful Affirmation

-
-
-

Healthy yummy snacks & meals

☐ ☐
☐ ☐
☐ ☐

Prayer Needs/Wants

Memory verse of the week:

Kick butt To-do list

☐
☐
☐
☐
☐
☐

☐ 5 min Prayer ☐ min
☐ 10 min Bible Read ☐ min
☐ 15 min Walk ☐ min
☐ 30 min Me Time ☐ min

15 min Give back:

Pray For:

Goals and focus for tomorrow

Sweet dreams beautiful.
You were amazing Today!

I want to make my castle amazing.
Steps to making my castle amazing. . .

“The wise woman builds her house, but with her own hands the foolish one tears hers down.”
Proverbs 14:1

Date ____________ Day ____________.

3 Goals today

-
-
-

Prayer Needs/Wants

Memory verse of the week:

3 Things I'm thankful for

-
-
-

Kick butt To-do list

- [ ]
- [ ]
- [ ]
- [ ]
- [ ]
- [ ]

3 Phone calls to make

-
-
-

3 Powerful Affirmation

-
-
-

- [ ] 5 min Prayer
- [ ] 10 min Bible Read
- [ ] 15 min Walk
- [ ] 30 min Me Time
- [ ] min
- [ ] min
- [ ] min
- [ ] min

Healthy yummy snacks & meals

- [ ]
- [ ]
- [ ]
- [ ]
- [ ]
- [ ]

15 min Give back:

Pray For:

Goals and focus for tomorrow

Sweet dreams beautiful.
You were amazing Today!

I am a warrior and a conqueror!
I will RISE ABOVE!
I will laugh in the face of my giants.
I will SMILE, for HE is with me, and we Only Know VICTORY!

“The Lord is with you, mighty warrior.”

Judges 6:12

Date ____________________ Day ____________________.

3 Goals today

-
-
-

3 Things I'm thankful for

-
-
-

3 Phone calls to make

-
-
-

3 Powerful Affirmation

-
-
-

Healthy yummy snacks & meals

- [ ]
- [ ]
- [ ]
- [ ]
- [ ]
- [ ]

Prayer Needs/Wants

Memory verse of the week:

Kick butt To-do list

- [ ]
- [ ]
- [ ]
- [ ]
- [ ]
- [ ]

- [ ] 5 min Prayer
- [ ] 10 min Bible Read
- [ ] 15 min Walk
- [ ] 30 min Me Time

- [ ] min
- [ ] min
- [ ] min
- [ ] min

15 min Give back:

Pray For:

Goals and focus for tomorrow

Sweet dreams beautiful.
You were amazing Today!

My past is the past. I walk in victory.
I walk in grace and beauty.
I hold my head high as my crown glistens.
Joy and Praise are on my lips. I dance.

"To bestow on them a crown of beauty instead of ashes, the oil of joy instead of mourning, and a garment of praise instead of a spirit of despair."

Isaiah 61:3

Date ____________________ Day ____________________.

3 Goals today

-
-
-

3 Things I'm thankful for

-
-
-

3 Phone calls to make

-
-
-

3 Powerful Affirmation

-
-
-

Healthy yummy snacks & meals

- [ ]
- [ ]
- [ ]
- [ ]
- [ ]
- [ ]

Prayer Needs/Wants

Memory verse of the week:

Kick butt To-do list

- [ ]
- [ ]
- [ ]
- [ ]
- [ ]
- [ ]

- [ ] 5 min Prayer
- [ ] 10 min Bible Read
- [ ] 15 min Walk
- [ ] 30 min Me Time

- [ ] min
- [ ] min
- [ ] min
- [ ] min

15 min Give back:

Pray For:

Goals and focus for tomorrow

Sweet dreams beautiful.
You were amazing Today!

I am going to do Great and Mighty things today!
I am strong and courageous because God is with me.

"Have I not commanded you? Be strong and courageous. Do not be afraid; do not be discouraged, for the Lord your God will be with you wherever you go."

Joshua 1:9

Date ______________________ Day ______________________.

3 Goals today

-
-
-

Prayer Needs/Wants

Memory verse of the week:

3 Things I'm thankful for

-
-
-

Kick butt To-do list

- [ ]
- [ ]
- [ ]
- [ ]
- [ ]
- [ ]

3 Phone calls to make

-
-
-

3 Powerful Affirmation

-
-
-

- [ ] 5 min Prayer
- [ ] 10 min Bible Read
- [ ] 15 min Walk
- [ ] 30 min Me Time
- [ ] min
- [ ] min
- [ ] min
- [ ] min

Healthy yummy snacks & meals

- [ ]
- [ ]
- [ ]
- [ ]
- [ ]
- [ ]

15 min Give back:

Pray For:

Goals and focus for tomorrow

Sweet dreams beautiful.
You were amazing Today!

Today I WILL eat Yummy Healthy food!
I will take care of my mind and my body by. . .

"Taste and see that the Lord is good;
blessed is the one who takes refuge in him."
Psalms 34:8

Date ____________________ Day ____________________.

3 Goals today

-
-
-

3 Things I'm thankful for

-
-
-

3 Phone calls to make

-
-
-

3 Powerful Affirmation

-
-
-

Healthy yummy snacks & meals

- [ ]
- [ ]
- [ ]
- [ ]
- [ ]
- [ ]

Prayer Needs/Wants

Memory verse of the week:

Kick butt To-do list

- [ ]
- [ ]
- [ ]
- [ ]
- [ ]
- [ ]

- [ ] 5 min Prayer
- [ ] 10 min Bible Read
- [ ] 15 min Walk
- [ ] 30 min Me Time

- [ ] min
- [ ] min
- [ ] min
- [ ] min

15 min Give back:

Pray For:

Goals and focus for tomorrow

Sweet dreams beautiful.
You were amazing Today!

I will have Peace today!
I'm giving Him my troubles. . .

"Peace I leave with you; my peace I give you. I do not give to you as the world gives. Do not let your hearts be troubled and do not be afraid."

John 14:27

Date ____________________ Day ____________________.

3 Goals today

-
-
-

3 Things I'm thankful for

-
-
-

3 Phone calls to make

-
-
-

3 Powerful Affirmation

-
-
-

Healthy yummy snacks & meals

- [ ]
- [ ]
- [ ]
- [ ]
- [ ]
- [ ]

Prayer Needs/Wants

Memory verse of the week:

Kick butt To-do list

- [ ]
- [ ]
- [ ]
- [ ]
- [ ]
- [ ]

- [ ] 5 min Prayer
- [ ] 10 min Bible Read
- [ ] 15 min Walk
- [ ] 30 min Me Time

- [ ] min
- [ ] min
- [ ] min
- [ ] min

15 min Give back:

Pray For:

Goals and focus for tomorrow

Sweet dreams beautiful.
You were amazing Today!

I'm writing down all the situations I need to handle today.
Lord show me how to handle these with wisdom!

"If any of you lacks wisdom, you should ask God, who gives generously to all without finding fault, and it will be given to you."

James 1:5

Date ______________ Day ______________.

3 Goals today

-
-
-

3 Things I'm thankful for

-
-
-

3 Phone calls to make

-
-
-

3 Powerful Affirmation

-
-
-

Healthy yummy snacks & meals

- [ ]
- [ ]
- [ ]
- [ ]
- [ ]
- [ ]

Prayer Needs/Wants

Memory verse of the week:

Kick butt To-do list

- [ ]
- [ ]
- [ ]
- [ ]
- [ ]
- [ ]

- [ ] 5 min Prayer
- [ ] 10 min Bible Read
- [ ] 15 min Walk
- [ ] 30 min Me Time
- [ ] min
- [ ] min
- [ ] min
- [ ] min

15 min Give back:

Pray For:

Goals and focus for tomorrow

Sweet dreams beautiful.
You were amazing Today!

"Rejoice always, pray continually, give thanks in all circumstances..."

1 Thessalonians 5:16-18

Date ______________ Day ______________.

3 Goals today

-
-
-

3 Things I'm thankful for

-
-
-

3 Phone calls to make

-
-
-

3 Powerful Affirmation

-
-
-

Healthy yummy snacks & meals

- ☐
- ☐
- ☐
- ☐
- ☐
- ☐

Prayer Needs/Wants

Memory verse of the week:

Kick butt To-do list

- ☐
- ☐
- ☐
- ☐
- ☐
- ☐

- ☐ 5 min Prayer
- ☐ 10 min Bible Read
- ☐ 15 min Walk
- ☐ 30 min Me Time

- ☐ min
- ☐ min
- ☐ min
- ☐ min

15 min Give back:

Pray For:

Goals and focus for tomorrow

Sweet dreams beautiful.
You were amazing Today!

Write a list of people you'd love to hang out with.
Write a list of people you need to distance yourself from.
(Those that are toxic, harmful, or destructive)

"As iron sharpens iron, so one person sharpens another."

Proverbs 27:17

Date ________________ Day ________________.

3 Goals today

-
-
-

Prayer Needs/Wants

Memory verse of the week:

3 Things I'm thankful for

-
-
-

Kick butt To-do list

- [ ]
- [ ]
- [ ]
- [ ]
- [ ]
- [ ]

3 Phone calls to make

-
-
-

3 Powerful Affirmation

-
-
-

- [ ] 5 min Prayer
- [ ] 10 min Bible Read
- [ ] 15 min Walk
- [ ] 30 min Me Time
- [ ] min
- [ ] min
- [ ] min
- [ ] min

Healthy yummy snacks & meals

- [ ]
- [ ]
- [ ]
- [ ]
- [ ]
- [ ]

15 min Give back:

Pray For:

Goals and focus for tomorrow

Sweet dreams beautiful.
You were amazing Today!

How can I show Love. . .
to Myself, Strangers, and those I know?

"God is Love."
1 John 4:16

Date ________________ Day ________________.

3 Goals today

-
-
-

3 Things I'm thankful for

-
-
-

3 Phone calls to make

-
-
-

3 Powerful Affirmation

-
-
-

Healthy yummy snacks & meals

- [ ]
- [ ]
- [ ]
- [ ]
- [ ]
- [ ]

Prayer Needs/Wants

Memory verse of the week:

Kick butt To-do list

- [ ]
- [ ]
- [ ]
- [ ]
- [ ]
- [ ]

- [ ] 5 min Prayer
- [ ] 10 min Bible Read
- [ ] 15 min Walk
- [ ] 30 min Me Time
- [ ] min
- [ ] min
- [ ] min
- [ ] min

15 min Give back:

Pray For:

Goals and focus for tomorrow

Sweet dreams beautiful.
You were amazing Today!

Write down things you love, people you love. How you love to dress and look. Places you love to go.
Then look to see if your Life is reflecting your heart.

"As water reflects the face,
so one's life reflects the heart."

Proverbs 27:19

Date ______________________ Day ______________________.

3 Goals today

-
-
-

Prayer Needs/Wants

Memory verse of the week:

3 Things I'm thankful for

-
-
-

Kick butt To-do list

- [ ]
- [ ]
- [ ]
- [ ]
- [ ]
- [ ]

3 Phone calls to make

-
-
-

3 Powerful Affirmation

-
-
-

- [ ] 5 min Prayer
- [ ] 10 min Bible Read
- [ ] 15 min Walk
- [ ] 30 min Me Time

- [ ] min
- [ ] min
- [ ] min
- [ ] min

Healthy yummy snacks & meals

- [ ]
- [ ]
- [ ]
- [ ]
- [ ]
- [ ]

15 min Give back:

Pray For:

Goals and focus for tomorrow

Sweet dreams beautiful.
You were amazing Today!

Things that make me sad. . .
Things I still grieve. . .
I will be Comforted by the Comforter because...
He LOVES ME!

"Blessed are those who mourn.
for they will be comforted."

Matthew 5:4

Date ______________ Day ______________.

3 Goals today

-
-
-

3 Things I'm thankful for

-
-
-

3 Phone calls to make

-
-
-

3 Powerful Affirmation

-
-
-

Healthy yummy snacks & meals

- [ ]
- [ ]
- [ ]
- [ ]
- [ ]
- [ ]

Prayer Needs/Wants

Memory verse of the week:

Kick butt To-do list

- [ ]
- [ ]
- [ ]
- [ ]
- [ ]
- [ ]

- [ ] 5 min Prayer
- [ ] 10 min Bible Read
- [ ] 15 min Walk
- [ ] 30 min Me Time
- [ ] min
- [ ] min
- [ ] min
- [ ] min

15 min Give back:

Pray For:

Goals and focus for tomorrow

Sweet dreams beautiful.
You were amazing Today!

Write down how you want to look physically. . .
What is my style, my signature look, scent, or hairstyle?
What do I want people to see when they look at me?

"She is clothed with strength and dignity; she can laugh at the days to come. She speaks with wisdom, and faithful instruction is on her tongue."

Proverbs 31:25-26

Date ____________________ Day ____________________.

3 Goals today

-
-
-

Prayer Needs/Wants

Memory verse of the week:

3 Things I'm thankful for

-
-
-

Kick butt To-do list

- [ ]
- [ ]
- [ ]
- [ ]
- [ ]
- [ ]

3 Phone calls to make

-
-
-

3 Powerful Affirmation

-
-
-

- [ ] 5 min Prayer
- [ ] 10 min Bible Read
- [ ] 15 min Walk
- [ ] 30 min Me Time
- [ ] min
- [ ] min
- [ ] min
- [ ] min

Healthy yummy snacks & meals

- [ ]
- [ ]
- [ ]
- [ ]
- [ ]
- [ ]

15 min Give back:

Pray For:

Goals and focus for tomorrow

Sweet dreams beautiful.
You were amazing Today!

I leave the past and its regrets behind.
I know today I am NEW in all things!
The past is the past and
I don't live there anymore.
I am living for TODAY!

"Therefore, if anyone is in Christ, the new creation has come: The old has gone, the new is here!"
2 Corinthians 5:17

Date ________________ Day ________________.

3 Goals today

-
-
-

3 Things I'm thankful for

-
-
-

3 Phone calls to make

-
-
-

3 Powerful Affirmation

-
-
-

Healthy yummy snacks & meals

- [ ]
- [ ]
- [ ]
- [ ]
- [ ]
- [ ]

Prayer Needs/Wants

Memory verse of the week:

Kick butt To-do list

- [ ]
- [ ]
- [ ]
- [ ]
- [ ]
- [ ]

- [ ] 5 min Prayer
- [ ] 10 min Bible Read
- [ ] 15 min Walk
- [ ] 30 min Me Time
- [ ] min
- [ ] min
- [ ] min
- [ ] min

15 min Give back:

Pray For:

Goals and focus for tomorrow

Sweet dreams beautiful.
You were amazing Today!

My plans to make TODAY great. . .
My plans to make MY LIFE GREAT...

"For I know the plans I have for you, "declares the Lord", plans to prosper you and not to harm you, plans to give you hope and a future."

Jeremiah 29:11

Inspirational Notes

"A thankful heart heals a troubled mind."

-Faerie Grace

Inspirational Notes

"Give your dreams a deadline so they can Live!"

-Faerie Grace

Inspirational Notes

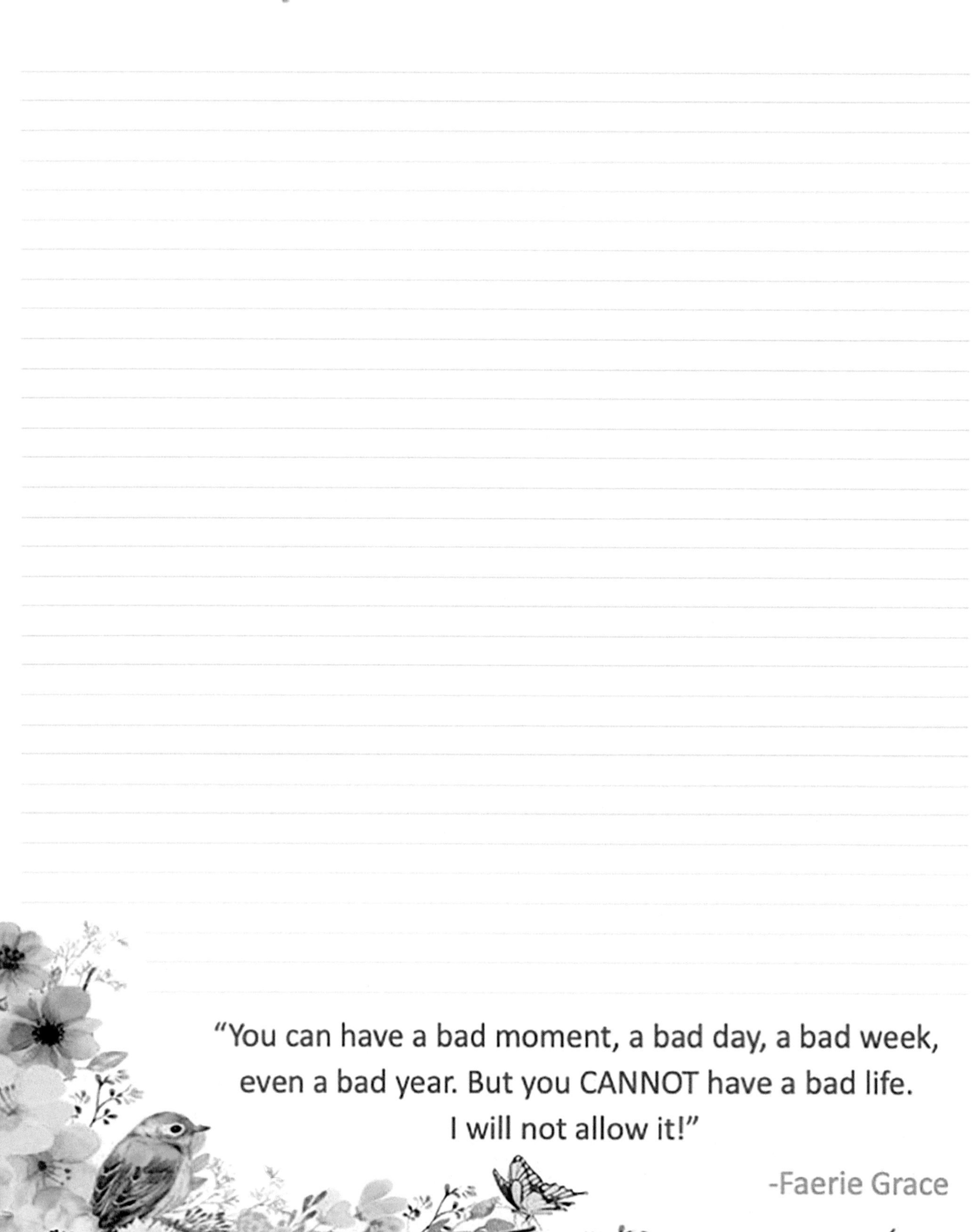

"You can have a bad moment, a bad day, a bad week, even a bad year. But you CANNOT have a bad life. I will not allow it!"

-Faerie Grace

Inspirational Notes

"Dreaming is in my soul, believing is in my heart.
My trusting is in HIM."

-Faerie Grace

Inspirational Notes

"You said, I couldn't. I believed you. But then I did it, and that made me smile."

-Faerie Grace

Inspirational Notes

"Write to Inspire, speak to Inspire, live to Inspire."

-Faerie Grace

Made in the USA
Monee, IL
17 October 2021